Journeys of a Long Walk

Brandy "Lade Breez" Elam

Published By Express Me Poetry

ExpressMePoetry@gmail.com

ISBN: 978-1-7345803-0-3

DEDICATION

To My Sons, Landre, Blake, and rest well Blessyn, I pray that I always make you proud I'm your Mom! You gentlemen are my greatest accomplishment.

To My Wife Ajeenah, my son Kaiden, and my baby girl Kyla, thank you for adding more joy to my life.

This is dedicated to the little girls in every adult woman who only wanted to be protected in a world that wasn't meant to protect them.
Baby girl you are more than they want you to see.
Shine unapologetically.
Breez~

CONTENTS

ACKNOWLEDGMENTS

To My Mother Sandra, Brian, Jackie, Larry, Ashley and Brittany

Rest in Peace Antonio

Ericka Winston (Lambda Zeta Phi Nu Fraternity, Inc)

Wayne Wheat

Georgia Fort (Sir Boxing)

Tierica Berry (A Woman's Standard)

Danita Gibson Lloyd (DGL Communications)

Shataia Brownlee (My Econ)

Kenneth Harris (DJ T- Rexxx)

ODE TO POETRY
Thank You for saving Me

Poetry brings people together/

Needing an outlet/ to just let it go/

Words move thru souls/

Like hot knives thru butter/

What other way should they/

Lines locked like Jamaican dreads/

They stick in your head/

Knowing not to cut them/

Because that's where your strength comes from/

Through the storm/is where they bring you from/

Eyes closed tight/

Minds open wide/

Receive this poets mild taste of the wild/

Words running free like antelope in the Serengeti/

Let it be/

Let it be your long walk through hell's hottest fire/

With not one burn or ill intention/

Let it be/

You brightest sunrise/

When the darkness has come/

Feed on words layered heavy with thoughts of the sweetest melody/

Let it be your reason for believing/

This entire world is not as messed up and they make it seem/

Things could be worst but you made it through to the end when/

You did want to give up/

Gratefully certain things in your strength won't let that be enough/

So u push on/

Holding on to the strength that you feel has come from where it all went wrong/

Giving u just a few more steps/
u hold on/

May be on an uphill battle/

But you fight for your place to belong/

Before long/

Victory at last/

You have it all/

Words is where it came from..

Brandy~

Introduction

12/29/2016

Today, I prepare to send my two small children, Lucas and Braylen, back to their father, Lucas Sr. At the end of September, I decided I had to let them branch off away from me so that I could truly focus on getting mentally and physically better for them.

In mid September I was injured at work and became medically unable to fully care for them. I could barely stand up straight, the pain was unbearable and I was physically dependant on those around me or lack thereof.

The mental strain took its toll on me. Fifteen years and I have been the only person my children have had in their lives consistently. 2016 claimed a lot of triumphs and pain for me and I've never been able to be naked and exposed as I will be to you. It's crazy how things surge your thought process in the middle of chaos and uncertainty; regardless of tears of joy or sorrow.

The elder generation tells you that time will heal all wounds, but it never specifies exactly how much time it will take. It never gives you ample opportunity to have a finish line to look forward to. However it comes, my life was always a combination of joy and pain from the youngest age I can remember; playing carelessly with my cousins in a small shack off of Rt. 41 in Richmond, Ga.

IRONY IS

Irony is/

Coming from a bloodline of champions who are only winning at being fools/

Supply tools to build nations within legacies of jealous hearts/

Families that fall apart when big mama dies/

Unfortunately the division was already set/

Bet on all of great grand mama's land/

They'd rather sell it than/

To allow it wrath beyond their time/

Blind visions of I'm better than/

The same sisters I shivered in the cold with/

The same brother I hungered with/

Would rather see their own progression/

Than progress within Building foundations that aren't even shakable by earthquakes/

Hatred starts in the homes and not in the streets of strangers/

The dangers were given at birth/

And regardless of how bad this hurts/

My family got this disease worse/

Blood only makes you related/

Degraded and treated like a ghost/

A build up of secret mental curses/

But never support when it's supposed to be your family in your corner/

Harm Presents them as monsters under the bed/

Replayed nightmares harass your dreams like your favorite movie/

Never spoken of again because those secrets could destroy the rest/

But your rest is never important/

And you never really rest again/

You never really live again/

Childhood scars that curse your every positive thought/

Knocks down every open reach for the skies/

It was only love to be after/

Again the years move faster than the recovery/

The assumptions weigh greater/

And the only comfort you get is not an apology/

Just a prayer they repent/

Become grown carrying those same burdens that haunted you since/

Sins that aren't even mentionable in church/

Just go to church

Until they are carrying you to the hearse to bury their secrets with you/

Thrown In the dirt by your next of kin/

But the irony is/

The realization of love lost isn't spoken until roses cover coffins/

Slow walking down memory lane of the good times had/

Often we skip the flower given when it can actually be

received/

Messages that can never be read/

And in the back of your head/

You pondering/

Wondering/

Foe or friend/

The worst hardship comes from your next of kin/

The same blood line generated by big momma's sweat and tears/

Destroyed memories and fears/

Generational disconnections/

Irony is/

It's always caught too late/

Debate if you must/

Ask yourself/

Just ask yourself/

When was the last time you remembered getting over your childhood/

Brandy~ Lade Breez

CHAPTER 1
WELCOME TO RICHMOND

Summer, August 1977
When things were so simple

Living with my Great Grandmother Ulonda, My Grandfather Jackson Earl, Grandmother Annabelle, my two favorite aunts, Gloria and AngelMay, uncle Derrick, an older Cousin who was close in age to Uncle Derrick, named Branden, two of my age relatable cousins, Trevor who's nine And Kay she's eight, my oldest Brother Bernard who's ten and I'm Beverly! I just turned eight this past spring, but you can call me Bev for short.

As you pulled into the front of the small house, it was onto a red dirt road driveway shaped like a half moon, that looped around to exit from the other side; it appeared bigger to us because we were so small.

Since there wasn't any indoor plumbing, there was only a

water spout outside that centered the front yard, close to the main road that catered to our every in house need. The water spout stood in front of an old tall oak tree.

You met the great porch first that was no entry unless grandma and grandpa were entertaining company.

All of their fine furniture, couch and love seat with perfectly shaped high backs with red silk and lace, that looked like they were from Paris, beautiful lamps that stood tall on end tables with marbled tops, fur rugs that where white as snow, thick satin curtains that draped down to the floor and curio cabinets full of irreplaceable imported China sets that made anyone feel like you were in one of those great houses that you couldn't touch anything in, because you feared the worst backside lashing of your life.

That great room had another non entry bedroom where grandma kept all of her clothes that she had collected from over the world.

Hats that matched every purse, and shoe, and Grandpa's fine 3 piece suits, hats to coordinate with Grandma and his extended collection of Stacy Adams shoes, all nested staged out of the way of us rambling kids.

In the back yard, where we mainly played, had this Grand Pecan Tree that gave us the best place to play hide and seek, and when the pecans grew, they were the best pecans you could ever have.

That great tree also marked where the low grass ended, and the beginning of the Rolling fields that lasted far as the eye could see; sweet grass that we could pick up from anywhere we stood was the outside delicacy while we played.

Rolliepollies, butterflies and an old dog that our grandmother's sister, Great Aunt Maggie let us keep that we called Mac. If we were lucky enough, Mac would bark when the big trucks would pass and we would all go running to the front yard up by the main road and pump our fist up and down. When the truckers saw us, they'd pull on their horns that echoed throughout the house until we couldn't see them anymore.

In the back of the house was another smaller porch and door where we could run inside straight into the kitchen and bother the older idle family members and get rushed back outside with a switch for playing and running around the house.

The kitchen had another bedroom that sat directly in front of the doorway where 2 big king size beds sat side by side which all of the kids shared. We girls slept with Great grandma and my Uncle and the boys slept in the other; a big set of drawers we all shared that sat on the far side of the room against the wall, and a small colorless television we shared if none of the elders were around.

If you walked further left in the bedroom off the kitchen, you would walk into another bedroom where Aunt Gloria and Aunt AngelMay shared.

Papa and big Mama of course rested in the off limits room with all of their things.

Daily life was normal for us kids. When we came home from school, we took off our school clothes to change into play clothes, did our homework, cleaned up before grandma and grandpa came home and would have to collect used milk jugs to fill with water for the night in order to make sure dinner could be made. After we ate together as one big happy family, grandma would go over our studies with us.

I think the most chaotic times in the house is when we would prepare for bed by pulling out a small tin tub that we would wash up in one by one; since we all had to use it, the fight would always be over who would go first.

No, we didn't have any complaints other than who would go first but the love over flowed. We always left the little home, clean, full and assured someone cared the world for us.

Grandma, who we all called Big Mama, would be gone a lot taking care of this old fragile white lady named Mrs. Denvil. Mrs. Denvil's family unfortunately owned the majority of Richmond.

Sadly, there wasn’t any amount of money that would make her kids care for her. Big mama would sit with the old woman and take care of her as if she were kin; then, at day's end, Big Mama would come home, tired and all but would make sure that after dinner we had our time; she would check our homework, make sure we read books and then put us to bed. Our education was the most important thing we could have in big mama's eyes.

Grandpa would leave late in the evening working at the local wood mill fifteen hours a day. He always came home smelling like fresh pine, but he never came home without peach pop and crackerjack popcorn for us as long as we had a good day in school. Life was simple. Life was easy. The life of a child, but there were responsibilities.

Early in the morning hours, there would be a knock on the room door before sunrise; before the rooster had a chance to sing his morning song. Papa Jackson Earl would bring big boxes of wood from work for the small furnace that kept the house warm and to cook or warm water for bath time.

If we were lucky, we could keep the big tall box; and when we came home from school, both my cousins, my brother and I would take the bottom out, then, like hamsters on the play wheel, we would tunnel our way out into the open field! That was the best game in the world to us.

In the early morning hours, we would have to help papa unload all of the wood, the boys would have to cut it in half, and us girls would have to neatly stack the wood beside the house.

Afterwards, we would feed and clean out the chicken cage, grab fresh eggs for breakfast and then head back inside to finish cleaning up, before washing up and preparing for school.

Great Grandma Ulonda, who we called Granny, was very limited to what she could do. Of Indian descendants, Standing no taller than 5'0, she had the most smoothest coco brown skin, long silky, salt and pepper hair that she wore in one braid that came down to the ground, light brown eyes that could see anything we were doing no matter where she was in the house, and the most gentle voice that would usually be our weekend wake up calls, because she loved singing in the mornings.

We could all sit in her lap and get the best kisses and hugs. Great Grandfather died before we were born. After 14 children, I think she earned the right to be taken care of for the rest of her days.

Granny was very forgetful, so she was limited to what she could do and couldn't be left alone. Sometimes she would even get lost inside of the house. Pending on which adult was around they would guide her back to her favorite chair to make sure she was ok.

Granny had good and bad days, but on her great days, she would sit us all down and tell the best stories about her childhood. Those were the lasting memories she never lost. It was amazing to see how she could recall things from her childhood as if it were just a day ago. Her stories were so vivid.

Grandpa was always so serious and stern. I didn't meet many people who weren't scared of him because of his size and demeanor. Even as a black man in the south, there was a great deal of respect for him by the locals.

The entire house could be in chaos, but when he said "be still", his voice echoed through the house like thunder. After he spoke, in the midst of silence you could hear a mouse crying in the corner the house was so quiet.

A deacon of the church, Grandpa stood 6'5 flat footed, broad shoulders, clean cut, ebony brown skin, and could hang a suit like no other, but a country boy to the heart.

Grandpa grew mostly everything my grandma put on the table. I don't know much about my grandfather's past. Grandpa never really spoke too much about it. The main thing we did know was his parents were killed by a lynch mob. My grandpa and his little sister survived the attack out of the nine family members. He didn't speak too much about it; but the hurt was so evident in his eyes.

His eyes could pierce your soul if you looked deep into them. At the age of fifteen he had to become the man of his house. He was the epitome of. Grandpa took care of his sister until she married and he met my Grandma.

Papa's motto was

"if men don't work, he's not a man and so he won't eat".

Papa made sure every boy and young man in the house knew how to lead a household. I think those traits are what drew my big mama to him.

Big Mama always said,

"He made more moves than a jackrabbit, but it was how gentle he was when it came to me".

Big mama was grandpa's "coca cola"! When he called her Cola, her smile was brighter than all the stars in the skies. It was amazing how he still made her blush after all those years.

Very petite, and only about 5'4, beautiful honey brown skin, long sandy red curly hair, always dressed to make heads turn, Big mama was beautiful. She spoke very gently but you knew when she meant business.

Other women in town were jealous of her figure even after her children; she had the perfect number eight shape. Big mama met papa when she was 16, and by the time she turned 17, Papa had went to her parents and asked for her hand in marriage. She became his wife a few months later.

Auntie AngelMay was who I wanted to be just like! She was a nurse in the local nursing home. She was 21, Small in frame, no taller than 5'5, long curly sandy red hair, and she resembles Big Mama the most, and all of the local young gents wanted the chance to court her, but she was stubborn as a bull.

Papa kept her occupied with studies because she was going to be the first doctor in the family. Every day when she came home from work, we all got any type of jello we wanted, and as many chocolate chip cookies we could eat.

Her schedule was a lot of work, study, and school. If she had the time she would show me what she was learning and teach me things at the same time. I loved our time together.

Auntie AngelMay was such a free spirit; and unlike the normal, "woman should be married by a certain age" stereotype, that was the last thing on her mind; she was purely career driven.

Uncle Derrick and Brenden were in their last year of high school and two of the most popular, most handsome and most athletic guys in the entire county. They were also the pranksters, which meant all four of us were subject to being a victim of theirs once or twice a week.

Uncle Derrick played football and ran track at the local high school. Branden played basketball and also ran track at the same school. They were both as tall as Papa. Uncle Derrick was caramel tan in complexion and Brenden was the smooth milk chocolate in complexion.

They were both very well groomed, to make sure they maintained their image; most of the school thought they were brothers, not uncle and nephew. Academically, they were both very intellectual, and physically, they were both great with their hands.

Bernard, Trevor, Kay and I sometimes had bad days. Even though we loved being at Big Mama and Papa's house, we were still troubled by not being with our moms and dads.

Trevor and Kay's Mom and dad, Debra and Clarence were in the Navy, Me and Bernard's Mom and dad, Sophia and Russell were in the Air Force.

At that time, we didn't fully understand why they had to be gone so often from us. Some days we would all cry together because we missed them, but Auntie Gloria wouldn't allow it to last long. Auntie would start making funny faces to make us all laugh hysterically, and after we played she would help us send "I miss you" letters that we decorated ourselves. Auntie Gloria was the best!

Auntie Gloria's dream was to always be a teacher. She was everyone's first teacher, and great with children. She's my big mama's first born; the dependable one; the leader.

All of us smaller kids would go to her for anything we

needed. Auntie Gloria was about 5'3. Coco brown skin and kept her hair neatly tucked in tight curls. She has the biggest beautiful brown eyes that you could really get lost in; but her smile could light the rooms of millions.

Her husband Uncle Christopher, Branden's father, had gone off to pilot school. After he got his wings, he was gone quite often, so Aunt Gloria moved back in with Big Mama so they could save up for Branden's college tuition. Also, since Uncle Chris was gone so often, I think it helped Auntie so she wouldn't be alone raising Branden alone.

Things were perfect.

Everyone was happy.

How does the saying go?

"When it rains, it pours?"

I'm not sure if either of us were prepared for this hurricane

I guess either this is the time you will either, sink or swim.

Drowning isn't a pleasant feeling at all.

Lade Breez Quotes

"In the midst of the mental madness, control the rage, or it will control you.

Allow your pen to be the weapon, fight it out"

BE A CHILD

Living life as a child makes you invincible/

No real life worries other than the games you will play at the end of each day/

All necessities provided without asking or having any wants/

No sense of regrets/

Except/

The extra toys and gifts children require because they feel like they need it/

But what we needed/

Was the strength of a family given without payment/

The power of love that required no monetary compensation/

The over excessive payment of unconditional love /

But from above, the reassurance of blessings in abundance/

Heaven sent angels on earth/

Granted without asking at birth/

Family for short/

Placed strategically to make sure you succeeded/

Lade Breez~

CHAPTER 2
CAN A FAMILY SURVIVE

December, winter 1978

You can't prepare for this.

It's Monday, and us kids have started our days off the same; early morning wood work and school, but our Grandparents are at odds end. Granny has a doctor's appointment in two days to check on a new medication. The million dollar question is who's going to take her?

Auntie Gloria and AngelMay have to work, Papa of course wouldn't take the time off from work because he is the head of the house hold, and the ornery old woman who Granny takes care of wouldn't dare to allow her the time off for personal business.

Granny can't miss this appointment regardless, so Big Mama calls all of her sisters to see who can get Granny there and on time. Out of the five sisters, Annabelle, Maggie, Sara, Wilma and Sheila, everyone is busy except her youngest sister, who is chosen to handle the task. Great Aunt Sheila hasn't worked a day in her life because her husband, Great Uncle Chuck, says she shouldn't. Uncle Chuck says "She is spoiled because she followed my instructions". All of the older sisters insisted, Of course she can do it. Problem solved.

Later on that night, Granny yells from the back porch while we are outside playing after dinner time and says,

"Anybody up for an adventure?"

Bernard, Trevor, Kay and I all scream

"YAAAYYYY!!!"

In unison!

With full excitement in our stride, we all charge forward towards her. She giggles with pride in her heart, and seemed happier than we were as she stares at our happiness stampeding towards her. If you could have seen the joy in her eyes you would have smiled as we did.

Granny slows us down and says,

"*Slow down babies, go wash your face and hands and gather around the big chair.*"

"*Yes ma'am*" we say.

We all run to the small face tub racing one another to be the first back to Granny's big chair. Of course Bernard, being the oldest of us four, was first, and then the rest of us followed.

We gathered around the big chair waiting patiently for granny to get to her chair. Her small fragile frame appeared from around the corner out of the other room. Slowly making her way to the chair, smiling her entire trip, there was this apparent excitement written across her face. She places both her hands on each arm of the chair and softly places herself centered perfectly into the seat.

"*Are ya ready?*" She asks with the brightest glow on her face.

"*More than ready Granny*" says Bernard.

"*Story, story*" chants Trevor.

Kay and I just expressed our eagerness with the light in our eyes.

We sat there, what felt like hours intently tuned in to Granny like we were watching our favorite cartoon. Granny told us a story about her childhood on the reservation. Granny told us how all of the men would leave going fishing and hunting early every morning and how the women would stay behind preparing for the great feast the entire village indulged in at each day's end.

Granny told us about how she and her sisters were the first women in the village to learn how to fish. It was so prideful to know Granny and her sisters never conformed to their expectancies.

There wasn't any other story that compared to our favorite which was "The Great Red Wolf story". And on this night Granny acted as if she didn't want to share it with us, so jokingly she says,

"*Ok, pick out a good book*!"

Kay says,

"*Granny, aww no*"

in a whimpering voice.

The rest of our faces turned sad.

Then giggling Granny says "*Got you!*"

We all laugh and I say, "*Granny tell us about Red Wolf*!"

She started,

"*Red Wolf was the Chief of my village. He was the greatest leader and had been Chief since my mother was a child. Very wise, all of the village Warriors and elders would gather around the sunset fire and discuss the protection of the village. On this particular winter day, Red Wolf was uneasy about some troubles he felt were afoot. Red Wolf gathered all of the village warriors around the great fire. He explained to them,*

"All Warriors need to be on high alert; something is stalking our village, and for the next three days, make the preparations not to hunt for the fourth day".

The next morning all hunters went out to gather fruits, vegetables, berries, fish and deer. The women villagers stayed home preparing the huts for the children and for their men to return. On the second day, they repeated the same. The morning of the third day, the warriors left as they did the two days prior leaving only Red Wolf, the village women and children.

Red Wolf instructed the women to keep all the children inside, me included. What we didn't know was, there was a pack of mountain lions that had been stalking the village. Which was strange, because mountain lions are loners, you know?"

We all shook our heads like we knew, and braced intensely to listen further.

"It was like Red Wolf could smell them coming. The leader of the pack smelled out Red Wolf like he felt the Alpha Male in him, while the other mountain lions surrounded the village. The lions all strategically placed themselves to cover each area of the village.

Red Wolf had only his bare hands to protect himself, while the rest of the village and the other mountain lions looked on preparing for the battle of the two. Red Wolf had the look of determination in his eyes, as well as the alpha lion, as they circled each other waiting for the other to attack. Red Wolf waited, and in haste, the mountain lion advanced at Red Wolf. They wrestled for what seemed like hours, and Red Wolf fought calculating, but bravely".

Granny explained the importance of The Heroic Chief waiting for the first strike, instead of striking first.

She said "*the angry man strikes first, keeping him off balance which also means he's not strategizing because his anger has him raging, and not thinking clearly. This also means he's more concerned about winning the battle instead of the war."*

Red Wolf used that discrepancy to his advantage.

"The lion continued advancing Red Wolf. Strong and mighty, Red Wolf continued knocking the Alpha lion down. Once the lion was exhausted, and had given his last burst of energy and sensing his defeat, Red Wolf had the mountain lion in his grasp with the tightest grip around his jugular; the strongest mountain lion of his pack, in a chokehold that had the Alpha lion paralyzed.

As the lion took his last breath, it was like the other standing lions took their last breath of hope. They stood in shock watching their leader's last moments like the petrified woods."

While Bernard, Trevor and I sat in disbelief and awe, Kay bravely spoke up inquiring,

"Granny, what did the other lions do?"

Granny then stands in a reflection of pride and boldly says,

"They retreated! Red Wolf defeated the entire pack by taking on the Leadership of the pack. The other village warriors were still out hunting. He stood alone without any of his war ready men, and not because he didn't know it was going to happen, but because he was our leader."

We all stared in amazement momentarily until Bernard asked,

"Granny, do you think I'm that brave?"

Granny replied, *"Yes baby, you all are. Remember to wait for the world to show you how it's going to attack, and then use its own anger against it, and as long as you don't give up, you will rise victoriously.*

The End."

Trevor begged for another story and we all concurred with his request. Granny insisted on preparation for bed instead and we all knew we didn't go against what she said regardless of our excitement, so we did just that.

Shortly after the story and bath time, Granny tucked us

all in and we fell asleep peacefully, anxiously waiting to hear what story Granny had for us the next day.

Tuesday morning, all of us kids woke up as usual to prepare for the wood unload and school. Granny was already up singing and cooking breakfast for everyone. Big Mama was getting dressed for work. Uncle Derrick and Branden were already gone to school. AngelMay was at work, and Aunt Gloria patiently waited for us to get dressed so that she could drop us off at school, so that she could be on time for her first morning class.

We considered it a normal day. We finished getting dressed then sat and had breakfast. After getting as many hugs and kisses as we could from Big Mama and Granny, we all raced to Auntie's car. Auntie Gloria, got us to school, gave us all 3 quarters a piece, and sent us to class.

At the end of the school day, Bernard always comes to each of our classes to make sure we walked together to the curb in front of the school to wait on Auntie AngelMay. Auntie picked us up on her lunch break to get us all home.

Granny was there with the brightest glare in her eyes when we got to the back porch. It was like she had so much clarity. Granny was so happy to see us and we were very happy to see her as well. Granny led us all inside, asking about our day in school, and giving us play clothes to change into.

Auntie AngelMay grabs some fruit and a sandwich and rushed out headed back to work.

Once we finished getting changed, we sat at the kitchen table to start on our homework and had a snack as we worked. Granny had retreated to her big chair to allow us to focus on getting as much done as we could without any help. On this particular day, we didn't need any help and we finished it all with ease.

Shortly after we were done, we placed all of the completed work in a pile for Big Mama to look over once she got off, cleaned up our mess from our snack and then rushed outside to play with the wood box Papa had left for us earlier.

Granny wanted to be out with us too, so Bernard and Trevor moved her big Chair out to the back porch so that she could keep an eye on us as we played.

Later that evening, all of the elders and Aunts had made it home from their busy work days. Uncle Derrick and Branden were out in the front yard playing football with a few of the other boys from their school, and dinner was cooking.

Bernard, Trevor, Kay and I decided to get an early jump on bath time while we waited, just in case Granny had a story surprise for us. Big mama looked over our homework, while we tracked outside to fill the water jugs so we could start warming water.

After dinner, Granny went to bed early. Instead of a Granny story, Big Mama read us a bedtime story and we all lay down for the night as well.

Wednesday morning, we didn't wake up to the usual singing from Granny. Instead, Auntie Gloria woke us up and got us ready for school. Big Mama was preoccupied helping Granny to remember where she was. Even though we were worried about her, we all finished getting dressed and sat at the table for breakfast. As we were leaving, we still went over to get our hugs and kisses from Granny. Something strange happened though.

Granny would always say,

"See you later Alligators"

And we would say,

"After awhile crocodile".

Instead, Granny told us,

"Goodbye", and held us so tight, kissed our foreheads and sent us out the door.

Big Mama waited for her sister, Aunt Sheila to pick Granny up for her appointment. Once Aunt Sheila got there, Big Mama let her know how challenging the morning was for Granny. Aunt Sheila was worried about not being able to be as calming as Big Mama was with

Granny.

Aunt Sheila had so many questions. She was so nervous. Big Mama assured her she will be ok; but just keep a close eye on her. Aunt Sheila agreed, took a deep breath then she and Granny left headed to the doctor's appointment, and Big Mama went off to work.

Dr. Ivan was the only doctor's office in Richmond who specialized in Granny's condition. Dr. Ivan had been Granny's doctor since she was diagnosed.

Aunt Sheila walked Granny into the quaint doctor's office and signed her in for the appointment. The office reeked of moth balls and aftershave.

The out dated flora patterned wall paper screamed update me to the 70's and get me out of the 1930's. There was a dusty plant in the corner that sat on top of an old used corner table and only enough chairs for four people to sit comfortably; and the television could only play the news channel.

The check in nurse was very short and disconnected in conversation; almost like she was forced to be in the front of the office. Her rusty blond hair and yellow skin seemed to prove she drinks more of the funny juice instead of water. Her teeth were even yellower.

Shortly after checking in, thankfully the nurse walked Granny and Auntie to the back into her room. Once they were situated in the room, Dr Ivan comes in and explains to Auntie Sheila he has to run a few scans on Granny before prescribing the medication.

Considering the process would take an extended amount of time, if she needed to, she could run a few errands in the mean time. Auntie agrees, gives Granny a kiss on the cheek and leaves Granny in the room with Dr. Ivan.

Mrs. Denvil had 4 boys in all, and all of them were trouble. The average privileged brats, the only one, the oldest; Jimmy Jr. escaped with some type of education to stand on his own two feet without the assistance of inheritance.

Johnny, who as the second child, was in and out of jail since he was younger. Jason who was the third, stayed in Richmond to drain his mother every chance he could get for money and Jonathan Denvil who is the youngest of the clan, was the very same.

Jimmy Sr. died a few years back of lung cancer because he smoked two packs of cigarettes a day. When he finally realized he was sick, it was already too terminal to fix, leaving Mrs. Denvil to continue raising four unruly, unskilled, entitled to the world brats or as the world would call them, “good ol boys”.

Wednesday morning, Jason and Jonathan went on their usual beer and liquor run to the store. Big Mama said by the time she got to Mrs. Denvil's estate, they were already half liquored up and high as a Georgia pine. Heading right in to clean up the mess the two troubled boys left, Big Mama was just relieved they had left for the day shortly after she came in to work.

Jimmy Jr. phoned in a few hours later to check on his withering mother and asked if the younger boys were out seeking employment. Big Mama let him know her thoughts of the liquor store being more important to them than a job interview and returned the phone to Mrs. Denvil.

Big Mama went on to do house work and prepare a meal for Mrs. Denvil. Once Big mama was done cooking she fixed the old woman a plate and sat quietly reading the daily newspaper.

Meanwhile, Jason and Jonathan were out drunkenly joy riding showing off their new pickup truck.

Dr. Ivan finished up the test he needed to run on Granny before Aunt Sheila could get back to her. Dr. Ivan tells Granny,

"Ok sweetheart, imma let you sit in the waiting room until your daughter comes back, I'll see ya next time ok?"

Granny nods, and the ornery nurse escorted Granny back to the waiting room and told her to sit tight until Auntie Sheila returned.

Dr. Ivan needed to give Auntie the new prescription that needed to be hand delivered to the local pharmacy; and explain the procedures Granny had done today, so he also reminded the nurse to make sure Auntie Sheila comes to see him before they finished checking out. The nurse had other patients, so she resumed her schedule checking on the other waiting guest.

Jason and Jonathan had so much alcohol in their system they nearly hit a few parked cars. Jonathan warned Jason to pay attention to the road jokingly before he ran someone off the road. Jason laughed it off and requested his brother pass him another beer. Jason had so little regard to the law; he was running traffic lights and stop signs like they didn't exist.

The two daredevils came around the corner in town too fast and before he could pop his beer he dropped it on the floor by the brake pedal.

Jason reaches as it continues to roll around under his feet. Jonathan laughs at him for his clumsy mistake and tells him to hurry up and get it before it gets stuck under the gas pedal.

Swerving profusely Jason leans over once more to grab the rogue beer can. Jonathan laughing hysterically was also paying more attention to the beer than the way they were traveling.

Suddenly, a loud crash from the front of the car distracted

the two from their hunt for the beer. They had struck something in the midst of their search.

Jason with fear in his voice asks,

"What was that, did I hit something?"

Jonathan unsure either, replies

"I'm not sure; I think you just run over a dog or something?"

Oblivious to responsibility, instead of stopping to check, they kept going. They speed off a few more feet, and the object is dislodged from under the vehicle.

Onlookers however, see a small body lying in the street. Rushing over for help, a townsman screams frantically for someone to call 911. Another woman came over to offer any assistance she could while waiting for the ambulance. Onlookers stood around in shock and praying the person was ok.

The townsmen covered the body and protected them so they wouldn't be moved. Once the ambulance got there it was too late; there wasn't a pulse. There wasn't any movement at all. Only the sounds of sirens; chatter from the emergency response team, but the crowd was so silent.

Auntie Sheila returns to the doctor's office and the nurse is sitting back at the front desk.

Auntie asks the nurse,

"Is Granny finished, and what's all the commotion out front? There is someone lying under a sheet and police are everywhere and even an ambulance."

The nurse, unaware of the tragedy outside, shrugs and replies,

"Well ain't she sitting out there? That's where I left her!"

Very snide and patronizing.

The two women look at each other in shock and instantly Auntie frantically starts going through the rooms in the office. Once she made it back to Dr. Ivan's personal office she demanded an answer as to where Granny was. In shock Dr. Ivan didn't have an answer for her. Auntie dropped to her knees. Even though she hadn't been back outside to the hit and run accident she prayed and prayed,

"God please, no!"

As swiftly as possible, she gets to her feet and runs as fast as she could to the body lying in the road. The small figure was still there along with the townsman because the area is now considered a crime scene. Auntie Sheila pushes through the crowd trying to get a closer look of what she feared, but was stopped by an officer.

She pleaded,

"please, please tell me this isn't a little older woman with

a long braid of hair down her back, please tell me it isn't; tell me this isn't granny!"

The officer's face turned pale and he replied unable to make eye contact,

"*Ma'am, if you know this woman you have to wait for the Coroner, I'm sorry*".

The townsman caught Auntie before she could hit the ground in the worst anguish possible and the tears flowed like rain. The pain was so agonizing; there wasn't any sound to her cry.

By the time the body arrived at the coroners, all of Granny's girls were together waiting to identify and confirm if the body was indeed Granny's. Word had already spread to the households, so all we had were prayers of it not being her and that she's just missing. It could be anyone. She's just lost and trying to remember how to get home.

We were wrong, we were all wrong. They pulled the cover from over her tattered and injured body to see what they all dreaded. Granny had been struck by a pickup truck and left in the middle of the street to die alone. They didn't stop to check, they didn't try to put her in their truck to get her help; they just left.

I wondered what her last thoughts were before she was hit. I wondered if her day had started to get better. I wondered if she knew that morning something was going to happen. I had so many questions. I had so many emotions. I was so angry. How could this have happened? As a child though, you know to remain silent regardless.

We weren't ready. The family became so divided with blame and anger. Granny's girls were so bitter with grief, they argued the entire evening after leaving the coroner's office. Auntie Sheila felt responsible because she didn't stay with her. Big Mama agreed with her because she told her to make sure she stayed with her, and Aunt Maggie, Aunt Wilma, and Aunt Sara All just cried and argued along with them.

What were we as kids supposed to do? They didn't care to see how bad we all were hurting from this loss. All we could do was cry and retreat to the room with Aunt Gloria, Uncle Derrick and Aunt AngelMay for comfort and they needed comforting themselves. They were strong for Branden, Bernard, Trevor, Kay and I. The pain was unbearable.

The fighting intensified until finally we heard silence after Papa spoke to calm down the bickering. Papa's voice was so easy, yet so stern that even our room silenced. He told everyone to calm down and focus on what needed to be done. The angered sisters did just that.

Moments into the calmness there was a knock on the door. Papa answered to find the sheriff on the main porch. Seconds later he was accompanied by all of the sisters. The townsman saw who hit Granny and left the scene. He was able to give them a description of the pickup truck and who it belonged to.

The emotions filled the room with horror; all of the sisters and Papa left following behind the sheriff. We sat in silence just shocked and numb.

When the sheriffs, Papa and all of the sisters got to the Denvil estate, part of Granny's shirt was still lodged in the front grill of the truck. Jonathan and Jason had passed out in a drunken stupor at home unaware and without a care of the chaos they had left in the streets of the city. They had to be summoned a few times before waking up. They were nasty and mean and still inebriated. The boys even started demanding the sheriffs to get out of their house.

The heathens were taken into custody kicking and screaming without any cooperation. It was intolerable for Big Mama and she collapsed. She cared for their mother and they murdered hers and left her lying in the street.

The next morning we woke up to more screams and panics after a phone call. The phone rang, Auntie Gloria's husband, Uncle Christopher had been killed in a plane crash.

Lord please have mercy. We can't take anymore. Within twenty four hours, death had visited out family and took numbers. Without any regard for our needs, without any regard for the hurt it would cause. The smiles and laughter that echoed through the halls of the tiny house were no longer. Silence became so overwhelming. Within hours, our family was stricken with grief.

Auntie Gloria wouldn't come out of her room with Brendan. Her cries were heartbreaking. We had never seen her sad before. She was always the happy to our day. We didn't know what to say to Brendan.

Big Mama didn't cry at all, she planned. For a week and a half, Big Mama made all of the arrangements. Granny was buried after the first week. Family gathered to say their last goodbyes and pay respects. I was able to hold her hand one last time before watching them lower the top of her casket to close it. We had so many family members all over the house after the recession.

The different age groups gathered in their small circles. The elder men, in suit and tie, cigars and whiskey flasks; the elder women in their hats, and hand fans, and us kids, we were just floating around kind of still in disbelief she was gone.

As the extended family members started to slowly leave. Kay and I went around to the front of the house to watch the cars leave Big Mama's. We didn't really speak to each other; we just sat holding each other's hands and stared off. I didn't know what to say and honestly, I don't think she did either. I'm not even sure if anyone knew we had snuck off to the front. It was peaceful. It was quiet.

We sat for what felt like forever until we were blinded by a car's lights pulling into the yard. Auntie Wilma was the only one who had only one child. His name was Michael. He didn't pull around to the back as everyone else did. He stopped right in front of the porch where we were sitting.

He seemed like he was already here the way he was stumbling out of his car.

Kay and I looked on as he struggled to the porch where we sat. When Michael reached us, he plopped down in between Kay and me and slung his arms around us. He reeked of cheap liquor and cigarettes.

Mike was really an outcast in the family. He was always in and out of jail, and could never really maintain a job. Mike was his own worst enemy because he was given every chance in the book by Auntie Wilma.

Mike graduated in the top percentile of his class; and he received a free ride to college; one out of the three black men in his class to receive an academic scholarship. After his sophomore year, he was introduced to drugs. Soon after, he dropped out of college and it was all downhill from there.

Mike eventually went from being career driven to being a career criminal doing anything for his next fix of drugs.

Kay and I were surprised he was there. We didn't see him often. Unfortunately, we didn't know any of the things he had going on. We didn't know he was a plague. We just knew he was our big cousin Mike.

Mike sat with Kay and I until Kay decided to go around to the back. I was never nervous about being around Mike. He was always the cousin who would show us cool things before he left for college. He was different but I didn't know how much. We sat on the big porch talking and laughing until he asked if he could show me something that he thought was really cool. With everything that was going on, I figured why not. I said sure and followed Mike to his car.

He instructed me to get in on the passenger side while he climbed in the driver's seat. When I got inside the car it smelled horrible. The inside looked as if he was eating and staying in his car.

Mike's eyes lit up when he was preparing to show me what he considered to be a big deal. Mike reached over into his glove box and pulled out a gun. It was a small silver revolver. The handle was white wood and had designs on it.

I felt my eyes grow big and I was shocked because even though Papa had guns in the house, I'd never been this close to one. In amazement I said,

"Wow, Mike where did you get that from? What do you

even need one for? Is it loaded?"

Mike replied,

"*Cool right, I brought it off this guy off the street when I went to North Carolina. Wanna hold it?"*

It scared me to see a gun up close, but I was mesmerized; and even though I was skeptical, I said *"yes!"*

He instructed me,

"Be careful with it and aim it at the floorboard of the car so you don't hurt nobody; hell don't shoot me."

I did just that. Mike placed the gun softly in my hands. I gripped the handle with both hands and aimed it at the floor like I was instructed to do.

Mike looks at me and says,

"Now this is our secret right? You know we would both get into trouble if anyone knew I let you handle my piece. Yo big mama would have yo backside red as chicken blood and would jus skin me alive."

I laughed and said,

"I*t's our secret."*

I handed the gun back to Mike and was curious as to why he had it but I didn't ask any more questions about it.

Mike leaned back over to put it back into the glove box like it made him feel like he had super powers to have it. As I proceeded to get out of the car to head back to the big porch, Michael grabbed me by my arm and told me,

"You don't have to rush off"

I shrugged my shoulders and replied, *"Ok"*, and closed the door.

Michael turned the car radio on and we started listening to the Supremes. Michael started dancing in his seat and making faces to make me laugh; but I couldn't help but notice he had this strange look in his eyes. He slide across the seat of the Nova and got closer to me. Still making the funny faces and laughing and singing together, he stopped and to ask me,

"So do you think you can keep another secret?"

I replied, *"Yes"*

Michael looks me in the eyes and says,

"You are looking very mature for your age, how old are you now about 14 or 15?

I replied,

"Of course not silly, I'm eight and a half thank you very much!"

Michael slides a little closer.

"So do you have a boyfriend yet? I know you have to have a boyfriend; you're too pretty not to have a boyfriend.

"Ew! No! Boys are nasty, who would want one of those?" I said. *"I do like this girl in my class though. She's really pretty and she plays with me every day, and she gives me her pudding cups at lunch."*

Michael sits back and has a look of shock on his face and then the look kind of transforms into cynical. He sat quietly for a moment and then asks me,

"So are you trying to tell me you wanna be one of those dike girls? You too pretty to be a dike girl, you gotta grow up and get a husband like you are supposed to."

Not understanding what he was saying, I thought it was a disease or something. I had never heard the term "Dike Girl"; what is that even? I had no idea what it was and took offense to it.

I replied,

"No! Of course not, but I don't want to do any of that either."

Michael seemed like he became irritated and he became even more aggressive. He told me he couldn't allow me to become a dike girl and that he knew how to cure me.

At this point I just want to get out of the car. I'm no

longer comfortable. I'm no longer feeling like I'm just sitting with my favorite cool cousin who's supposed to protect me. I don't understand what he is saying because his speech has become more slurred. He keeps grabbing my knee and is now sitting with his arm around me. No longer comfortable, I attempt to get out of the car again.

He yells at me,

"DON'T OPEN THE DAMN DOOR AGAIN!!"

I felt fear. I closed the door. I tell him,

"I'm done listening to music Mike; I want to go back to the rest of the family now, let's go to the back with them; I'm sure Big Ma is looking for me now."

I start to grab the handle and he grabs me and locks the door. He reaches over me and grabs the car seat handle and leans it back towards the backseat. Tears start streaming down my face towards my ears.

All I kept thinking was; I'm going to get into trouble if I get my dress messed up. I didn't want to mess my dress up. I didn't want to accept the reality that I had put myself in this situation. It's my fault because even though you hear how the adults talk, you know to never interrupt.

The seat is leaned back. His right arm is behind my head and his hand is on my shoulder pulling me closer to him; he's putting his weight on me on my left side and I feel petrified.

Michael: *"Remember you said you can keep a secret? Imma show you what you are supposed to feel like being a woman."*

His left hand goes up my dress.

"You see this" with his hand between my legs, *"this is a woman's special place only made for a man, you hear me?"*

His tone is angry and forced. I close my eyes and clench. I want so badly for my mom to come knock on the car window. I'm looking for my Auntie Gloria, I'm looking for anyone; Papa, Kay, anyone. Please anyone.

His hand slides pass my rose colored panties. I feel his finger forced inside of me. I let out a yelp. Tears streamed faster down into my ears.

"Yea this is your treasure"

He kisses my cheek.

"Y*ou like that don'tcha? Don't cry, this is natural girl, you will be a woman after this"*

He continues to move his finger in and out of me. He is rubbing his self on me and making strange noises. I float off.

I don't feel anything. I don't smell his cheap liquor

anymore. I don't see the trashed car anymore. I don't see my cousin Mike anymore. He doesn't look like Mike at all. It's a monster. He's the devil.

It felt like hours. It felt like the minutes stopped to allow him time to finish transforming me. His grasp tenses up and he squeezes me the last time very tightly and there is a wet spot on him where he had been rubbing up against me. He removes his fingers from inside of me and leans back into the car seat with a plop.

His breathing is heavy and he looks over at me and reminds me,

"Remember, this is our secret, we don't want to get into trouble now do you?"

as he sticks his fingers into his mouth.

I don't remember replying; I pulled my dress down, and tired to make it longer to cover me up more. I opened the car door and got out. I closed the door and walked slowly to the Big Tree that use to seem so magical to me, and climbed up. I got to my favorite branch and didn't feel like I could sit on it any more. I climbed further up. I wanted to get away and there wasn't enough tree to climb. The branches held me.

I'm not sure if I fainted or went to sleep in the big tree; I just remember Papa and Uncle Derrick bringing me down out of it and everyone fussing because I had been missing for so long. That night, my bath was longer. The water was hotter. Sadly, I could never wash the dirt off.

My uncle Christopher had to be sent home, it took two weeks for us to have his service. Out of respect for our family, we were unable to open his casket.

Everything to me now, is only a blur. Anguish had its hold on our family in a way that felt normal it was so overwhelming. At the end of Uncle Chris's service, we all returned home to Big Mama's. Everyone is sitting quietly in the main room. No conversing, no radio or television playing; just silence. There weren't any words to be spoken. All of a sudden the house shook.

We hear a loud door slam shut in Big Mama's room. We've never heard her cry before; we've never heard her break before. It was deafening; it was heartbreaking. I pray to never have to hear that again. We all cried for her.

After completing her mission, and again making sure everything was taken care of, she could finally grieve.

Lade Breez Quote

“Your weaknesses are only kryptonite if you’re superman.

Be human.

Just keep learning to be better than your mistakes”

SURVIVE

We are never given a time or an hour of the last/

Past time with thoughts of what we want to be when we grow up/

Carelessly range from age to age/

Not knowing that growing up isn't promised/

Not knowing that minutes are numbered/

But for certain death is in good health and taking numbers/

Wild eyed to the weary/

Handling death of a loved one is like handling hot coal barehanded/

It burns holes in souls/

But living life with a dead soul is more damaging/

Numbness that becomes normalcy/

It breaks hearts in un-repairable pieces/

Leaving Broken hearts with none refundable warranties/

Children with unanswered questions/

Praying to God for answers/

In the midst of dead silence/

Begging to maintain sanity/

But what becomes of sanity/

There is no time limit on grief/

There is no anxiousness to grow up when the world is so ugly/

There is no hour glass of power/

There is no time relived/

Memories that play like movies in theaters/

Preparation time is unheard of/

Only memories of time shared/

Nightmares aren't spared/

But never a moment to prepare/

Living dead/

Lade Breez vs. Hurricane

CHAPTER 3
TROUBLE DON'T LAST ALWAYS

Spring, March 1979

What's Next?

Granny's death took a lot from the little home. Christmas wasn't filled with laughter and joy. Big Mama was so miserable now. Everyone was still grief stricken. The thought of going to the Denvil's place every day after those boys murdered Granny was taking its affects on Big Mama.

Shortly after their arrest, Jason and Jonathan were released from jail on bond. A few weeks after we laid Granny to rest, they pleaded out and didn't serve any time for her death. They murdered Granny and could walk the same street they left her laying on. It was like Granny's death wasn't important to the money and the power of the family who owed that little town. Justice was in the eye of the beholder.

They were given community service. Two months to the day of Granny's death, the boys lost control of that same truck they hit Granny with and it went up in flames. They're bodies were unrecognizable they were burned so badly. I guess it was all the alcohol they consumed that made them burn so quickly.

Big Mama continued going to the Denvil Estate everyday to take care of a woman whose children killed her mother in cold blood and left her there in the street.

Auntie Gloria was doing her best. I would sometimes catch her weeping silently to herself and I would give her a big hug. Branden wasn't his happy self any longer. We would always try to make him laugh, but Branden just couldn't.

Auntie Gloria did her best to keep him mentally on track to graduate, but the thought of Uncle Chris not being there when he walked across the stage was a heavy burden to bear. Thankfully it became his motivation. Uncle Derrick kept pushing Branden everyday telling him not to let it bring him down but to use what Uncle Chris had taught him to make him proud.

March means a lot to me because it's my birth month. This March just didn't seem to be as bright as the last. Regardless of how I tried to block out the night of

Granny's funeral, the more nightmares I had.

I didn't know how to feel. I was so embarrassed. I was full of so much shame. It was my fault. I got into the car with him. I promised to keep a secret. I promised. I have to be excited. I can't tell.

Focus! I have to be excited, right?

Birthdays were always exciting because our mom and dad and Auntie Debra and Uncle Clarence would send us all birthday gifts on each of our birthdays. It was like having four birthdays a year.

Bernard, Trevor, Kay and I would always try to guess what we would get since our parents traveled so much. My birthday is two weeks away and turning nine was a very big deal before that night in the yard, but I'm not certain I really care about getting older anymore. Everyone else is dealing with grief, and I'm being eaten alive by secrets. But the show must go on right?

Kay says,

"Bev, when I turned 9, we got bikes and wagons to play in the yard with, how do you think they are going to top that?"

Trevor replies,

"Well we got racing cars and you guys got dolls for mine, I didn't think that could be beat!"

Bernard interjects standing proudly,

"Well who got the four wheeler? As far as I'm concerned my birthday has been the best!"

We all stop to look at each other for a moment, and then I say,

"Showoff!"

We all laugh loudly and then continue to play.

In the midst of it all, I didn't feel like my happy go lucky self any longer. It's my birthday and my excitement is in comparison to getting a visit to the dentist for a root canal. However, every day we waited patiently for Big Mama to come home to see if we received anything in the mail.

We were so anxious; we didn't realize that we were only a few days away from my birthday. We were however, shocked because we usually get our gifts a few days before so that we could guess what was in the boxes until we were permitted to open them on the day of.

The boxes never showed up. I cried and cried the few nights before my birthday. Everyone thought it was because we didn't get any gifts; but in reality, I felt like everyone knew my secret. I felt like it was my fault we couldn't get gifts because I was wrong for allowing him to do that to me. I felt like it was too much.

Auntie AngelMay came in from working a later shift and I was still crying. She grabbed my hand out of bed and took me into the kitchen to go onto the back porch. I sat in her lap and she hugged me so tight.

"Hey, what is going on with you little turd? Your birthday isn't until the day after tomorrow, don't worry about the gifts, maybe the gifts are just late."

I couldn't hold it any longer. I couldn't stomach to keep quiet. I hold on to her tighter.

"Auntie, it's not the gifts, I don't want to be a woman anymore. I just want to stay a kid"

"Honey, that's a part of life. We all want to grow old, and start our own families to....."

I immediately interrupt her and just blurt it out without warning.

"But he hurt me, he made me keep it a secret and said I couldn't tell, he said I'd get into trouble; he said it was going to make me a woman. I didn't want to be a woman Auntie, I promise I didn't. But he forced his hand inside of my special place! He wouldn't let me get out of the car until he finished, he said that was what made me a woman."

I buried my face and cried harder. I couldn't stop the tears; it was like I relived it all over again.

Her face was no longer glowing in compassion; it felt like she was in so much shock she had stopped breathing. Her tight hug, turned into her hands gripped on my upper arms and her staring directly into my eyes.

"What do you mean, "HE", who the hell is "HE"!?"

Tears continued to swell in my eyes and slowly dripped down my cheeks. *"Mike, Auntie, he hurt me really bad, and I begged him to stop Auntie, I begged, but he didn't, he didn't stop until he was finished."*

"MIKE? MIKE? MY COUSIN MIKE?? OUR COUSIN MIKE?!?" BEVERLY!!! DON'T YOU EVER SAY THAT EVER AGAIN!! THAT IS A HORRIBLE LIE TO TELL ON YOUR FAMILY, AND I DON'T WANT TO HEAR THAT COME OUT OF YOUR MOUTH EVER AGAIN. NOW GO BACK BED!"

I can't remember when I had stopped crying. I can't remember when I stopped believing he was wrong. I just knew for a fact, it was me. It was my fault.

I got up, and I did as I was told. I went to bed. I never spoke of it ever again.

Who am I to correct any adult?

Finally it's the day before my birthday. At this point, it is over for me, but inevitable, I'm turning another year older tomorrow. Auntie AngelMay comes in from work and tells us all to come to her room with her. We all come in and sit on the bed. They are very excited because in our minds it means its present time! I am going to go with the flow.

Auntie AngelMay leaves out of the room once we are all inside sitting, and closes the door. A few minutes past and she comes back in and asks us,

"Are you ready for your surprise?"

They all scream loudly, "YAYYYYYYYYY!!"

Auntie AngelMay pushes the door open further, and standing behind her, were our parents! Words couldn't express the joy we had as we rushed over to them to give them the biggest hugs possible.

My dad picked me up and held me so tight, as mom kneeled down to hold Bernard. Trevor and Kay were just as excited to see their mom and dad too. Kay wrapped herself around her dad's leg so that she could catch a ride on his foot, while Trevor sat in his mom's lap hugging her tightly.

This was the best surprise we could have. Better than any gift they could have sent. We haven't seen each other since Granny's and Uncle Chris's funeral, so being together for a happy occasion was needed.

We all spent the day just laughing and listening to the

military stories from Dad and Uncle Clarence.

The next day was my big Day!! "Happy Birthday Beverly!!"

To me, this wasn't a big deal to turn nine as it was before. I have to be strong. It was my fault it happened; so get over it Bev. We all anxiously got out of bed to prepare for the festivities of the day.

Kay and I always wore matching clothes and Bernard and Trevor did as well. Big Mama said that's the best way to make sure we are loved the same.

Our dresses were pink, yellow and blue striped sun dresses, with shoulder straps that tied into a bow; we wore clear jelly sandals to complete the outfit. After we finished getting dressed, Auntie Gloria and Auntie AngelMay sat together and put our hair in five ponytails. Bernard and Trevor wore Yellow and Blue Collared shirts, blue shorts with anchors on them, long socks with a yellow stripe across the top and brown shoes.

Meanwhile, our parents were diligently preparing the back yard for the party. The Great Pecan Tree in the back yard became a "pin the tail on the donkey" center with pink and yellow streamers hanging from the lower branches. There were many games in different areas like jump ropes, Hula hoops, jacks and marbles and my favorite, kick ball.

Papa had already started the fire in the outside fire pit he built, to cook the chicken, ribs and burgers. Big Mama was in the kitchen baking my birthday cake. Yellow cake with chocolate icing was my favorite! Big Mama had a big pot of collard greens on the stove, corn bread, macaroni and cheese, and potato salad!

As guests begin to arrive, the fun increased. Our family is massive. We have so many cousins, uncles and Aunts. It was always so amusing to see how they all grouped off into their own sections of the yard.

All of the older men would be gathered around Papa at the fire pit comparing stories about who's barbecue's the best, while passing around the whisky bottle or flask they attempted to hide from their wives, and playing cards.

The older women would be seated in the shade under the pecan tree with their sun hats on, and hand held fans, mainly watching the children and laughing at the men who think they are hiding whisky from them.

The younger Aunts and cousins would be playing the games with us. Double Dutch was the best way to get our moms and aunts off the porch. My mom and Aunt Gloria would hold the ropes while Aunt AngelMay and Aunt Debra would "show us how it's done". The laughter was continuous.

As the kickball game took us into the later part of the afternoon, Big Mama and her daughters start setting out the food on the serving table. Papa yells out to the family,

"LET'S EAT!"

All of the kids rushed the kid's table and instantly got shooed away by Great Aunt May saying

"I know you all better go wash the dirt off your face and hands!"

We all ran around to the front of the house to the water spout where Auntie Debra was waiting with a towel to dry our hands and faces once we finished. After we all returned to the table the plates were set out, and we all listened to Papa's stern voice to say the grace and bless the food hand and hand.

Everything was delicious and not one plate had more than bones and fork scrapings left on them.

When we finished cleaning off the tables, Big Mama brought out the birthday cake with nine shining candles on top that were all different colors; while everyone else sang Happy Birthday; once the cake was cut, the kids went back to playing and the groups resumed their position in their bunched off areas.

As the sun began to set, Mom, Dad, Aunt Debra and Uncle Clarence called us over for us to open presents. I got to open mine first! We got new dresses, shoes, and cabbage Patch dolls. Bernard and Trevor got new baseball mitts and bats, and three piece suits that looked like Papa's. I also had five birthday cards with a dollar in each.

When we finished collecting our gifts, we cleaned up our gift paper and threw it away; we played into the later part of the evening until the elders began getting tired. The day was wonderful. We played until we were worn out.

After the last guests left, we begin our usual routine of collecting water to prepare for bath and bed time. Mom and Auntie Debra helped us with bath time while Aunt Gloria and Aunt AngelMay finished putting up the remaining food and cleaning the rest of the kitchen.

After bath, we all sat on the floor talking to our parents. Dad said that they had one more surprise for us. Excited we waited to see what it was. Uncle Clarence said that this isn't something we can open, so we were puzzled for a moment until Mom says,

"When school is out this year, you guys will be moving; we have brought houses for you to come and stay with us, we think it's time for you guys to have your own rooms!"

Mom and Aunt Debra decided not to reenlist back into the service and focus on family life. Dad And Uncle Clarence would continue their military careers.

At first we were excited, and hugging our parents, but then after further details, we realized we were being separated. Trevor and Kay would be Three hours away from where Bernard and I would be moving to. We had never been away from each other; other than to visit our other grandparents. How will we adjust to life? Even though we missed our parents, we were more like brothers and sisters, not cousins. It was surely going to be a difficult adjustment.

In May, everyone prepared for Uncle Derrick and Branden's graduation. There were so many people there. Their graduating class had three hundred graduates.

All of the men graduates including Uncle Derrick and Branden wore freshly pressed white collared shirts, black ties, slacks and shoes under their Burgundy cap and gowns. The young ladies wore White knee length white dresses with burgundy low pump heels and one single line of pearls under their all white cap and gowns.

Once the ceremony began, it took, what felt like forever, for all of the proud onlookers to calm down once the line of graduates proceeded.

The most touching moment and I think the highlight of the graduation, was when Branden walked across the stage. Branden was met by Uncle Christopher's three brothers and Uncle Derrick all hugging him in Uncle Chris's place.

Everyone had tears in their eyes, especially Aunt Gloria who was overwhelmed with joy and sadness; her tears ran relentlessly.

Uncle Derrick had already received his acceptance letter from Howard University and Branden was accepted into Morehouse University. The celebration was greater than any birthday party we had ever seen. Big Mama and Auntie Gloria didn't have to worry about tuition, they both received full scholarships.

This was bitter sweet for Bernard, Trevor, Kay and I though because this also meant it was also time for us to move away from each other. Uncle Derrick left a week after graduation and Branden followed a week later.

At the end of May, our parents came to the little house and packed all of our belongings. Kay and I cried and held on to Big Mama until we were placed in the car.

Trevor and Bernard sat in Papa's lap until they were told to say goodbye. We stared out of the window of the car at Aunt Gloria and Aunt AngelMay until the home we had known for our entire lives was no longer visible. What will life be like without the familiar?

What am I going to do without Kay? Who's going to help Papa with the wood now? Most importantly, who's going to take care of Big Ma?

New beginnings; and unspoken sadness, this move is looking promising already.

Lade Breez Quote

Decide to put the baggage down, carrying it is a choice. Lighten your load.

Decide to be Happy for you!"

CHANGES

The familiar seems so comfortable when compared to the unknown/

Fear insights mental restrictions locking doors without conclusions/

Illusions of blurred vision distort facts from fiction/

Slightest mentions of what use to be are like marbles swallowed by babies/

Breathtaking in the most violent array/

They say, you are young and this won't change your day/

Focus on making new friends and learning a new way/

Traumatizing excuses instead of resolutions on how to feel/

How to deal with sadness, the madness/

Cloaked my changes/

You are okay is what they tell you/

But you are not okay/

You are drowning in uncertainty and memories/

You are made to wash away true feelings/

Replace them with changes/

Well what am I to do with the anguish/

Brandy to Lade Breez~

CHAPTER 4
WHAT ABOUT A NEW ADDITION?

Summer 1981

Looking for the Rainbow after the storm

It's been almost two years since we moved away from Big Mama and Papa's house. Life was very different here in Charlotte, NC. The house our parents brought was very different than the little house off the dirt road in Richmond.

The tan house with blue shutters had three levels to it and sat on a hill, up a long paved driveway that you had to drive up to get to the garage with a fenced in back yard. There weren't any trees in the front or back yard, just a well groomed lawn that looked like every other lawn on the street.

We had never seen houses this close together before. If you stood in the kitten window, you could shake your neighbor's hand from their kitchen window.

Once you walked into the front door, you were in the middle of the house or front entranceway. To the right there was a Great Room that had all White furniture; a curio cabinet with fine china, and a grandfather clock. Mom wouldn't allow us to go in this room because she considered that her fine furniture for entertaining guest.

To the left was a downward staircase to go into the den where we could watch TV and play in our play room. The laundry room sat off to the left of the den and a half bathroom without a tub, just a toilet, next to it.

If you walked a little further pass the staircase down, there was another upward staircase. Up those stairs were a full bathroom that was to the left, two regular rooms, one for Bernard and one for me, and the master bedroom that had another full bathroom in it that was Mom and Dad's.

Straight ahead on the entranceway was the kitchen. The kitchen had a small breakfast nook in it where we ate the majority of our meals. To the left of the kitchen sat the dining room with the big Cedar dinner table we only used during holidays or special occasions. The door to the back yard was also in the kitchen.

My mom, Sophia Ann Johnson, is about 5'8, small frame

and through the Air Force, always stayed in great shape. She was very beautiful with beaming brown eyes, always keeping her sandy brown hair tightly curled and looks a lot like Papa with a caramel skin tone. Since she's been out of the Military, Mom decided she would go back to school for social work, while working part time in a daycare center while we were at school.

My dad, Russell Lenard Johnson, was an E-6 in the Air Force. Standing 6'2, dad was a very big muscular man. Curly black, well groomed hair, with brown eyes. Dad was mixed having a Caucasian mother and an Indian father, but he always held strong to his Native American side. Bernard and I didn't meet either of them while we were old enough to remember, they passed away when we were younger.

Dad was very meticulous and had to have everything a certain way, or it wasn't the right way. Dad was still gone a lot, so we didn't see him too often. He would come home every few weeks and stay for a few days and then leave again. It became routine to us.

My Parents meet in Junior college and enlisted together right after marriage.

Instead of riding to school in the car, we had to ride the bus with the other kids in the neighborhood. So early in the morning, mom would walk us down to the corner of the street and wait until Bernard and I got on the bus.

At the end of the day, Mom would be there when we got home to walk us back safely. After school we would still change clothes before starting our homework and daily chores before dinner.

Mom would multitask and help us with homework while preparing dinner. Once we finished our homework, Bernard and I would get a group of kids together to play baseball or tag football in the middle of the street.

There weren't many other girls in the neighborhood, so I spent most of my free time following behind Bernard. Which was ok with me, but I'm not too sure how Bernard felt about having his baby sister on his coat tail everywhere he went.

"We have something to tell you guys"

Dad came home a few days ago because we are on summer break from school. He's excited and wants to go out for dinner instead. Mom takes out the outfits she wants us to wear, and we get dressed.

Once everyone is looking their best, we all load into the car and head to Mom's favorite restaurant. We pull in to the parking lot and park close to the building.

Dad runs around to Mom's side of the car and delicately helps her from the car. Bernard and I follow behind them. Once seated, Dad allows mom to order what she wants and then he proceeds to give the waitress his order for

Bernard and I, and finishes up with his order.

Once the drinks come to the table dad looks at us and says,

"We have something to tell you guys!!"

His face was bright as the tree on Christmas and his excitement tickled mom. Dad takes mom's hand and looks at us and asks,

"How would you guys feel about being a big brother and big sister?"

Bernard and I look at each other in shock and then at mom. Mom now has tears in her eyes and says,

"It's true, you have a new little brother or sister on the way!!"

Bernard says,

"I hope it's a boy! I would love to have a brother!"

I said,

"No a girl, finally I'm not the baby anymore!"

We hug mom and dad tells the waitress,

"This is a celebration, once we are done with dinner, Bring the best cake on the menu!!"

After dinner, dad tells Bernard and me that we have to start taking more responsibility around the house to help mom. We agreed to make sure we did. We were all excited to find out what mom was having. Now that school was out we could help out a lot.

A week later mom and dad left us with a house sitter to go to the doctor's office to find out if it was a boy or a girl. Bernard and I waited in the front window for hours waiting on them to return!

When we heard dad's car coming up the drive way we took off outside to meet them at the garage too excited to wait until they came inside. They made us wait though.

"Hold on, hold on"

Dad says while chuckling at us both,

"Let me get your mother inside and comfortable, and then maybe we will tell you if all of your chores are done!"

And then laughs out loud.

Bernard says,

"Aw man come' on dad, tell us!! Please!"

We joined in chanting together,

"Tell us, tell us, tell us tell us",

While following close behind them headed into the house. Dad pays the house sitter so that she could go home. Mom goes down stairs and sits in the den while

Bernard and I are persistently begging for the information.

We hear the door close and dad walking down the stairs. He is still laughing at us. So he sits down right next to mom and the both yell,

"IT'S A BOY!!"

Great, another boy, just what I needed. Bernard is ecstatic. I, on the other hand, am not as excited as I would have been if it would have been a girl, but nonetheless I'm happy.

When we started going to school here, I wasn't really interested in making new friends. Every day I thought about how much I missed Kay and Trevor. The distance between us was almost unbearable when I had moments to sit and think about them. Even though the new baby would be exciting, it wasn't the same as the sister and brother I felt I lost.

Bernard and I would talk about them all the time, but it was easier for him because it wasn't hard for him to make friends. Bernard had plenty of guys to play with but I only had those guys to play with as well. They all adopted me as their little sister too. If I couldn't play the game they were playing I would sit on the green utility box at the end of the yard and watch them play.

One day the guys were playing football. If you wanted to

tackle you could as long as it was done in the grass. This wasn't a game I would play after learning my lesson the first time and one of the guys hitting me in the grass like I really was one of the guys. Nope, you couldn't get me to do it again. So I took my seat to watch them brutalize each other.

There was a house that sat right in front of ours. The lady who lived there didn't mind us using her yard as part of the playing field and would sometimes bring us out snacks and drinks. She was a foster parent and when the children she would foster would be placed away from her; she would give us the sweets and stuff so it wouldn't go to waste.

On this day, it wasn't the older lady who came out; it was a girl who looked my age. She looked very shy and stood at the end of the driveway directly across from me.

She stood for a moment watching my brother and his friends run up and down the street, then she ran back into the house. A few minutes later, she ran outside, waited for the boys to pass, then ran across the street to join me on the green utility box.

"*Hi, my name is Shanice, what's yours*?"

"*I'm Beverly, but you can call me Bev*!"

Shanice was a little shorter than me, long wavy black hair

that she kept in two braids to the back, and the prettiest smile I'd ever seen with two dimples that would always show. Very soft spoken and shy, but we told each other everything.

Shanice had been in foster care since she was younger. Her and her two sisters, Nicole and Tonya, had been separated and sent in different directions, so she felt alone a lot until she and I met.

Her mother used to beat her when she would get high on drugs, or if she couldn't get high. When the police found the three girls, they were bruised and starving after being left in a drug house for a week. She hasn't seen her mother since. She had no idea who her father was.

Shanice and I became inseparable. We would have sleepovers at each other's houses, we would play together every day until the street lights came on and we were forced to go inside. If you know anything, you know that when the street lights came on, your best bet would be to be inside.

Shanice loved to sing, so when we would be in our rooms together she would always sing for me. When school started back, we would walk to the bus stop holding hands. We would sit in the same seat everyday together; all of our classes where together too.

January 9th it happen, our baby brother was born. I was more excited about being able to stay with Shanice for that week, than finally having a new brother.

Dad was able to be home so that he didn't miss the birth. Bernard stayed with his friend Anthony. Mom let Dad name him "Russell Lenard Johnson Jr." When Bernard was born, mom only let dad make his middle name Russell.

If it were up to dad, all of his boys would be named after him. Bernard and I gave him the nickname RJ. Mom was just happy to have her body to herself again.

Now that RJ was born, mom was very busy with him for the first few months. Dad was only home for a short while to help mom settle in, but he was gone again by the time RJ turned a month old.

Bernard and I helped as much as we could so that mom wasn't completely exhausted. Shanice and I would watch him so mom could nap too. She didn't know that we would keep him quiet if he woke up before she did. I knew she needed the rest.

RJ was the sweetest little baby. He spent most of his time laughing and cooing when I made silly faces at him. Bernard was too scared to hold him while he was this little, but not me; it was fun seeing how he responded to me. I had plenty of help from Shanice too. She felt like he was her little brother as well.

Mom stopped working after RJ was born and just focused

on going to school. Most of her studies could be done from home, so she decided that was best for us all. The part time job was only a hobby to keep her occupied while dad was away.

Now that RJ is here, her time shortened. When he napped she did homework or made dinner or did things around the house that she couldn't do while he was awake. When she would cook or bake, mom would let Shanice and I sit in the kitchen and teach us how to make different things.

Shanice loved my mom like her own and often told me how she wished her mother was the same. Honestly, I felt blessed even more because I felt bad for her. I was all but too happy to share my mom with her. She was my best friend and I didn't want her in any more pain.

The school year went by faster than normal this year and it seemed like summer never ended. Bernard was happier now that I had a friend and didn't have to follow him around, RJ was six months now and becoming more independent. He was pulling up on his own and sometimes if you acted like you weren't paying him any attention he would stand up on his own too.

When he started making sounds his first word in my book was Bev. That's my story and I'm sticking to it. Mom said he said momma, but all moms hope their baby's first word is that.

Dad was sad because he was missing all of his first moments. Since RJ's birth, dad had only been home for a total of eleven days. We missed him, but mom always assured us it was his duty. It didn't make it easier, but we understood.

Our summer began and it started off amazing. On one summer day, Shanice and I decided to make a fort that was only for us; our hideaway from the world when we felt upset or discouraged or just for our girl talk.

In our back yard, the hill went up higher than the drive way and you could sit up there and see the entire neighborhood. We decided that spot would be perfect. We took some tree branches, rope, some old bed sheets that mom gave to us and a sheet of plastic. We built our fort at the top of the hill in the farthest left corner of the back yard.

We tied the tree branches together for the base, after that, we took one of the sheets to make it the roof and cover the branches; we took the rope and tied the sheets to the branches.

The plastic was the top layer to keep the rain out. Bernard and his friends helped out with that by hammering post into the ground to secure the fort for us. The rest of the sheets became the floor bottom for us to sit on with pillows; perfectly awesome.

We laughed and played together every day in our fort. It

had become our official meeting spot. One particular day, Shanice calls and tells me to meet her in the fort. I go up there and wait on her. A few moments later she comes in and we greet each other like normal. We position our snacks. We sit in the fort talking and she says,

"I have to ask you something."

Puzzled, I say,

"go for it."

So she's asks,

"Have you ever been kissed before?"

Horribly, my mind instantly takes me too the monster in the car. It made me cringe.

I say,

"no, never! Why? Have you?"

She says,

"No, but I want to try it, but only with someone I love."

I stare at her for a moment, which felt like forever; speechless and then say,

"Well who would that be?"

She moves closer to me and puts her hand in mine. My palms are sweaty and I'm shaking. When I grasp her hands, she is shaking like I am too, and her palms feel just like mine.

I move in closer to her. To this point, we have shared our deepest secrets. This feeling was different. I ask her again,

"Who do you love?"

Instead of replying, she leans in close to my lips. A trickle of sweat runs down the side of my face. My heart is pounding out of my chest. Her lips are so close to mine, I already feel her quivering with just as much fear as I had.

Her heartbeat was racing. She is breathing so hard our breaths synced. Her hand touches the right side of my face. I move in closer. Our lips touch.

At first we were eye to eye but, it was like we both let go. I wrap my arms around her waist. She holds my face with both hands. Her lips were so soft and tasted like banana lip gloss.

I had never experienced this feeling. I had never felt the tingling sensation in the pit of my stomach. It was comforting and peaceful. It was beautiful.

We sat in silence just staring at one another until it was time to go inside for the night. Our bond was sealed tighter than ever before. The time we spent together increased from that day forward.

Things seem perfect. The last month of summer was perfect because she had become the meaning of love to me. I had never had a crush, I had never felt this. I just knew I didn't want to stop feeling it.

A week before school started, Shanice and I sat in her room playing checkers because it was raining outside. Her foster mom made us sandwiches and gave us chips as a snack. Shanice was a sore loser though. I kept winning so she kept quitting and starting the game over.

The last game, I let her win just so that we could get through a full game. She knew I did, and attacked me tickling me until I had tears rolling down my face from all of the laughter.

A pillow fight pursued. We got caught up in playing so much we plumped into the bed laughing hysterically! After we put the game up, and remade the bed, we just sat and talked about everything, from our first day back to school outfit, to where we were going to sit on the bus this year.

Shanice got very quiet for a moment and I wondered what she's thinking. She has this "cat with the canary in his mouth" look on her face, a kinda smirk look. Then she finally said it. She says,

"It's you, you are the reason I smile, and I love you."

We hugged for what felt like the lasting comfort of

forever.

Unannounced to either of us, her foster mother had come into the room; she stood quietly watching us, before exiting just as quietly as she had came. She didn't say a word; she didn't even let us know she was there.

We asked if I could spend the night, but for the first time ever, her foster mom told me no. The foster mom said they had a busy morning ahead of them. Since this was the first time, we didn't press the issue, we hugged and said goodnight.

The next morning, August 28, 1982, I hopped out of bed. On a Mission, I started on my to-do list. Finished my chores in record timing; help mom with RJ and get dressed before mom could tell me what was supposed to be done.

Once she checked everything, I asked was it okay to go get Shanice. Mom said I had done a great job so it was ok that I went. I rushed out the door, down the hill, and headed to Shanice's front door. I pushed the doorbell and waited patiently for her to come to the door.

After a few moments had passed, I pushed the doorbell once more. Then I remembered, her foster mom said they had a busy day. Even though I was sad about it, I returned home to wait for Shanice to get back home. I'm still waiting.

Days passed and I have not seen or heard from Shanice. For a few days I attempted to speak to her foster mother without any luck. It felt like she would stay away from home until it was time for me to go inside, to avoid my unanswered questions.

Shanice was gone. I never knew heartbreak. There wasn't anything I could do. The depression was unbearable. How can you move on without any closure? How can you say goodbye when you didn't get the chance to say goodbye?

This was my first taste of heartbreak. I wish I could say it was my last taste. As the days passed, it became harder and harder. Shanice was a constant in my mind and dreams.

I wondered was she ok, I wondered where she ended up, and most importantly, I wondered if she thought about me too. Those questions are still unanswered. They still linger. Since I wouldn't talk about how I felt, my mom brought home a journal for me, and so it began.

Lade Breez Quote

"Don't risk your dignity trying to prove a point to fools. Arguing with them jeopardizes you as well."

UNBREAKABLE LOVE

How many millenniums does it take to express the extent of love towards one another/

How many shifting clouds can rain on any parade when you have learned to dance to the rumbling sounds of thunder/

Perfect drums/

Skies lit extraordinarily by lightening/

Still only basking in the minute/

Hours/

Years/

Even tears/

Being in Love is a balance of power/

Power between 2 people willing to sacrifice it all to be together/

Willingness to allow no other/

To come between the binding essence

of a connection that isn't breakable

by any human standard/

Withstanding all test and trials meant to destroy

the vision of how you see them/

But to them/

You are their world/

A pedestal only designed to hold them up

while they are at their weakest point/

Prided by every accomplishment achieved on their behalf/

And on her behalf/

Ready to stand in front of the firing squad

to protect the loyalty preserved for her/

Submissive to every I love you or just because moment/

Because on those moments/

God smiles on this Union like His completion of the world/

I miss you everyday He sends this way/

My mental is just stuck on giving you

This apology.

Lade Breez~

CHAPTER 5
HOW DO I RECOVER

Fall 1985

Dust Yourself Off

The summer I spent with Shanice still weighted heavy on my heart even years later after we were forced to separate from each other. I had no desire to get close to anyone. I had no desire to do anything for that matter. Honestly that was my first time meeting depression.

Mom would tell me that I would come out of my shell in high school, but 9th grade was the toughest year of school. In the 8th grade, you are considered the seniors of middle school. When you reach high school, it's like you have to start all over again from the bottom.

High school will either make you or break you to be completely honest. There are greater threats, there are meaner kids, and there are more classes and less people willing to help you get through it. Nonetheless, in my family, oh you are going to school.

The school was twice as big as the middle school, and classes were also just as big. Most of my classes, I positioned myself in the first row. The only class I had where I was forced to sit towards the back was math.

The teacher, Mr. Fields, had a horrible memory. Mr. Field was small in stature, but made up for it in intellect. Although Mr. Fields was small, he was very athletic in build. To help him remember our names, he placed us all in assigned seating alphabetically. If I would have had a choice, I would have preferred home schooling.

Bernard was two grades ahead of me, so he had already adjusted perfectly by becoming one of the city's top athletes since he played football so well. Bernard was the "Jock popular kid", and I got the shaded shadow title of being "Bernard's Little sister". Great!

Not only did I become the token football star's sister, not a soul would look my way since they were afraid of what the football team would do to them. Yes, just great indeed. (Inserts sarcasm and rolling eyes)

Most days I prayed I stayed invisible, but the majority of the time it was impossible. I wore big clothes, to hide my shape, I dressed like a tomboy and I loved playing sports; I tended to always be picked to do certain things, thanks to my brother being so well known and liked.

It just never mattered what I did or what I participated in, my mind would always take me through the emotional roller coaster of trying to figure out what was wrong with me. Why do I feel so strongly about girls? Why would I rather play football than play dress up or play with dolls?

For the life of me I didn't understand. They only thing I knew about girls liking other girls were that it was a sin and God hated anyone who did it. It was embedded in me every time I went to church and didn't want to sit pretty watching the young guys playing in the church field after service; I would mess my dress up playing in the mud just the same.

To make the school year move faster, I forced myself to engage in clubs so that I could stay out of my room longer; Future business leaders of America, National Honors Society, Chess Club, I played tennis and ran for the cross country track team. Whatever I could do to keep my mind occupied, I was all for it. Unfortunately, I didn't remain busy enough.

May 21st, the school year was coming to a close. Bernard and I came in from the bus and mom yelled from the kitchen for us both to come in and sit down.

We sat our things down on the kitchen counter, grabbed snacks, and sat at the kitchen table like she asked. Mom smiled, and asked how our day went at school. We told her it was good and proceeded to venture into everything that had happened throughout our final day at school.

Mom allowed us to talk her ear off for about fifteen minutes about every party and prank, every school yearbook signature and every teacher who was just happy it was finally summer break.

Eventually, she interrupted us and told us she had something very important to speak to us about. Mom told us that she and dad would be leaving in the morning and would be gone for a few days.

Puzzled, but not shocked, we sat listening. Mom would go on trips with dad often, so this wasn't a rarity, however, her announcing she would be gone, was.

Mom said everything would be different when they returned but Auntie AngelMay would be coming later in the afternoon to stay with us. Mom wanted us to be on our best behavior, help out with chores and make sure we helped Auntie with RJ. We agreed and ran up the stairs to prepare for Auntie's arrival, not giving Mom and Dad's secret mission another thought.

I went into the bathroom and I closed the door. After so many years, I haven't seen Auntie since I told her the malicious things Mike had done. My thoughts became so overwhelming. I could hear his breathing; I started hearing her screaming at me not to ever say it again. I never did mention it again. I never told Mom; I never told Dad. Suddenly, the bathroom had become that car all over again.

I instantly turned the bath water on, and I got into the shower. I needed to be clean. I sat in the tub for hours. I had to wash it off. I had to get clean. I had to breathe. I got myself together, and I got out of the tub. I put a smile on my face and joined the rest of the family down stairs to eat dinner.

After dinner, Bernard and I cleaned the kitchen while mom continued packing their things. Dad sat in the den yelling at the television while RJ played with the refrigerator magnets in the floor. In the midst of a water fight, the doorbell finally rang. Bernard and I rushed off racing to get to the front door. Mom yells down the stairs,

"STOP RUNNING IN MY HOUSE, YOU BOTH SOUND LIKE A HERD!!"

We giggle, and speed walk to the front pushing and shoving. We fling open the door, and start smothering Auntie AngelMay with hugs and kisses.

It had been a very long time since we had a chance to see Auntie on a happy occasion. We finished getting as many hugs as we could and then Bernard grabbed her bags and we escorted her into the house. After a few more hours of packing, mom and dad were ready to go.

They kissed Bernard, RJ and me goodbye and left. We sat for hours conversing with Auntie. There was so much to tell her. There were so many things I wanted to pull her aside to say privately. However anxious, I waited patiently for Bernard to get his fair share. She asked us so many questions too. Regardless of the issue, it truly was good to see her after so many years.

Later in the evening after Bernard and RJ went to bed, I walked down the stairs to get a cup of milk. Auntie was sitting at the table reading and finishing an essay diligently working.

I sat at the table next to her to try and seem interested but in actuality, honestly trying to get her to look up at me so that I can empty my thoughts about everything that I haven't been able to speak about since Shanice has been gone. Obviously she must have noticed; she closed her book and looked at me in concern.

"What is it turd?"

Before I knew it I was pouring my heart out about everything. I couldn't eat or sleep hardly thinking about everything that happened with Shanice.

Before I could catch either of the words coming out of my mouth, I had told her everything, including the kiss. For a moment she sat in a daze; I assumed from shock of what I had let out. She rubbed her head for a few minutes staring at me in silence. The silence was truly suffocating. Her head lifted from her hands and she said,

"Sweetheart, that was a demon on you, everything will be ok now; I'm glad that thang is gon from around you now.

Now your soul will be saved. You'll be just fine, ok? Just forget about her now, you will have bigger fish to fry na, gon back to bed baby, Auntie has to finish this paper by morning."

I didn't finish my glass of milk; it was probably room temperature by now anyhow. I looked at her with the blankest of stares for a few moments, then I stood to my feet, and I quietly walked back up the stairs back into my room. I closed my door, and I couldn't cry anymore. I could feel anything. I laid my head on my pillow, and I went to sleep.

The next morning, she didn't mention anything. She acted as if the conversation never happened. To this day I feel it was intentional when she asked Bernard, how many of his friends were hanging close to him, trying to be sweet on me; she was even overly conversing on boyfriends of the future and what type of wife I was going to be to the right man some day; ironic indeed.

Inadvertently, I felt molested again.

Auntie was with us for a little over a week. We would speak to mom and dad everyday but we were having a great time with Auntie doing what we were told; preparing for Mom and Dad to return.

Finally, on the day Mom and Dad were due to come back; Auntie told us that everything had to be perfect. She said that we had to make sure we continued to be helpful and do what we were told even if we really didn't want to do it. She kept exclaiming like mom was going to need our help the most.

After we completed all of our chores and cleaned the house from top to bottom, we sat in the main window of the house for what felt like forever waiting on their return.

To keep us busy, we played cards to pass the time. I beat Bernard in the last hand and in the midst of my own celebration, we see Dad pulling the car up the hill into the garage, but mom was sitting in the back seat. We take off running outside to the car and swing the door open to find mom smiling and grinning from ear to ear, and she speaks softly,

"Wait guys, I have someone I want you to meet."

In the middle of all the excitement we didn't notice that mom was holding a new little person. She pulls the small little pink blanket form over her face and says,

"Meet your new baby sister guys, her name is Blair Noel.

She was so tiny. We stood in aw for a moment, because it was so unexpected yet so great. She looks just like me. I have a little person that looks just like me!

Dad comes around the car and grabs Blair out of mom's arms and then helps her get out of the car. Mom was moving very slow and very carefully.

When RJ was born it wasn't so "careful". I grabbed mom's arm and went up under it and Bernard went up under the other. We all walked into the house so that Blair could see her new Home.

Wow I'm a big sister now with meaning is what it felt like. This pregnancy was a bit more complicated than I had seen mom go through. Her scar was very visible and she had to be very careful how she moved.

Blair had to be removed instead of mom going into labor like she did with the rest of us. Leave it up to the baby to cause the most stress. I made sure I didn't leave either of their sides. This was a very big deal.

I couldn't believe how much she looked just like me. Her eyes were so bright. Blair was so alert and observant. She followed me around the room with her eyes. I felt like she was sizing me up. Or maybe she knew I was the one who was going to teach her everything I could.

Either way, she wasn't going to have to worry about anyone harming her in any way.

I walked over quietly and I asked mom if I could hold her. She sends me to wash my hands and tells me to sit down in Dad's recliner. I walk over to the and anxiously wait for mom to lay her in my arms.

Her eyes are wide open and staring directly at me. I say,

"Hey sweet girl, I'm your big sister Bev, I'm here to protect you"

In my heart of hearts, I know she understood me. She smiled big and her eyes had so much comfort in them. I meant every word of it.

The excitement made me forget about some of the things I was hiding. I finally felt like I had something to look forward to that didn't involve lying to me on a daily basis. If God hates people like me so much, then why did he make me this way?

Lade Breez Quote

Healing begins with the acknowledgement of why you're hurting, but it doesn't justify why your hurt others.

Minor Thought Lesbian

Who Are You

Have you ever had to prove yourself/

Convince yourself that you can grow out of it/

Quiet thoughts haunt your emotions/

Pain takes ova/

Who are you/

You ponder over and over/

I'm 10 years old/

How can I feel this way about another/

Indications prove/

Your life has already been set up for you/

But who are you/

Explosive fights between morals and what's wrong, or what's right/

Can't sleep at night/

Who are you/

I turn 11/

And heaven only knows what little girls go thru/

Standing out like sore thumbs/

Flirt with the little boys or it becomes/

The worst year of your life/

In your mind you continually ask why/

Why is this happening to me/

Back then/

You didn't have bullies/

You had popular kids/

And momma ain't here/

She works 2 or 3 jobs/

With just enough time to check homework/

And a good night kiss/

But not enough time to inquire about how my day went/

Her day was spent/

So I took it/

Never saying a word/

But pushing my face in my school work/

Good grades were all I could pay/

And that's all she knew/

Who are you/

12/

Well I could say I barely made it/

Faded most parts from memory/

So that it wouldn't hinder me from forward motion/

Would call it torture but even animal poachers made better friends/

I would pretend like I couldn't hear/

My mind telling me you want a her still/

Society will rush u like a world wind/

So I stayed in/

Who are you/

I asked myself over and over again/

I haven't found that feeling about men/

My reply I don't want a boyfriend/

Preteen madness/

Had this best friend/

And for the world I wouldn't let her go/

We would hang thick as thieves/

Playing all day on the swings/

She told me my secret was safe/

Missing a day with her was all I could hate/

If I wasn't at her door when it was time to go outside/

She would be at mine/

She even taught me how to kiss/

Funny how time flies/

Summer seems longer when you had no one to play with/

Even longer for foster kids/

Who could never say where they would be at day's end/

And the next day/

She was gone/

No goodbye/

No I will write/

Not one call/

Her social worker had no worries about us/

My first taste of heart break/

and in the wake of it all/

I was alone again/

no new friends no new friends/

I needed that song back then/

Lade Breez~

Lade Breez Quote

Life is what you make it. Either you can be washed away by the storm, or you can learn to dance in the rain."

ABOUT THE AUTHOR

Brandy "Lade Breez" Elam is an Author, Philanthropist, Humanitarian, Motivational Speaker, Life Coach, Event Host, Mentor, youth tutor, and Spoken Word Artist out of Columbus Georgia by way of Detroit, Michigan. CEO of "Express Me Poetry" and founder of "Educated Blessyns", Lade Breez is not only active in the community for words but also for the Cause.. Actively involved in Her Community, Lade Breez is a Motivational Speaker for Mental Health and Well-being, an Activist for Black Lives Matter, Women Against Domestic Violence, The NoH8 Movements. Actively involved in numerous group home settings, Lade Breez is a Life Coach and Mentor of children ages 8-18 under her non-profit organization, "Educated Blessyns". Lade Breez is 2016, 2017, 2018 and 2019 Spoken Word Artist of the Year Nominee, 2017 and 2018 Spoken Word Artist of the Year, 2017, 2018 and 2019 Humanitarian Award Nominee, 2018 and 2019 Host of the Year Nominee, 2019 Women's History in the Making Community Leader Award Nominee, 2019 Curvy Alliance Recipient, and 2019 Sybil Johnson Woman Of Excellence Award Recipient. Lade Breez is above all else, a Mother, And a Wife. Lade Breez believes in "Improving this World one stage at a time" by maintaining strong Values in Family, Honor and the gift of helping others.

Brandy "Lade Breez" Elam is an Author, Philanthropist, Humanitarian, Motivational Speaker, Life Coach, Event Host, Mentor, youth tutor, and Spoken Word Artist

Made in the USA
Columbia, SC
22 June 2020